Best Practices in Reading

NEW EDITION

Level B

Best Practices in Reading, Level B, New Edition
OT126
ISBN-13: 978-0-7836-9330-9

Triumph Learning® 136 Madison Avenue, 7th Floor, New York, NY 10016

Printed in the United States of America.

15 14 13 12 11 10 9 8 7 6 5 4
HPS255474

TABLE OF CONTENTS

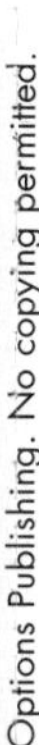

Photography Credits:
Abbreviations are as follows: t=top, c=center, b=bottom, l=left, r=right, bkgd=background

COVER: Library of Congress; 02 (t) ©PhotoDisc, Inc.; 03 (c) ©PhotoDisc, Inc.; 04 ©PhotoDisc, Inc.; 11 ©Corbis; 12 (tl) ©PhotoDisc/C Squared Studios/Getty Images, (cl) ©Foodpix/Burke/Triolo Productions/ Jupiter Images, (cr) ©PhotoDisc/Fototeca Storica Nazionale/Getty Images, (tc) ©PhotoDisc, Inc., (b) ©Burke/Triolo/Brand X Pictures/Jupiter Images; 13 (tl) ©Bettmann/Corbis, (cl) ©Bettmann/ Corbis, (tr) ©Corbis (cr) ©PhotoDisc/Spike Mafford/Getty Images, (b) ©PhotoDisc, Inc.; 14 (t) ©Doug Mazell/Index Stock Imagery, (b) ©PhotoDisc, Inc.; 15 (t) ©Foodpix/Burke/Triolo Productions/Jupiter Images, (c) ©Chip Henderson/Index Stock Imagery; 16 ©Photodisc, Inc.; 18 ©PhotoDisc, Inc.; 25 (t) ©PhotoDisc, Inc., (b) ©Tom Brakefield/Corbis; 26 (t) ©Richard Hamilton Smith/Corbis, (b) ©Farrell Grehan/Corbis; 27 (t) ©PhotoDisc, Inc., (b) ©Rose Hartman/Corbis; 28 (l) ©Joe McDonald/Corbis, (r) ©Tom Bean/Corbis, (b) ©Alissa Crandall/Corbis; 29 (t) ©W. Perry Conway/Corbis, (c) ©Darrell Gulin/Corbis; 30 ©PhotoDisc, Inc.; 39 Courtesy Johns Hopkins Children's Center; 40 Courtesy Johns Hopkins Children's Center; 41 (t) ©Detroit Free Press/William DeKay 5-15-88, (b) Courtesy Johns Hopkins Children's Center; 42 (t) ©Keith Weller/Courtesy Johns Hopkins Children's Center, (b) Courtesy Johns Hopkins Children's Center, (c) ©PhotoDisc, Inc.; 43 (t) ©Roswell Daily Record, Aaron J./AP Photo, (b) ©Detroit Free Press/William DeKay (5-15-88); 44 ©PhotoDisc, Inc.; 53 ©Artville; 54 (r) ©Peter Byron/PhotoEdit, (b) ©Bill Aron/PhotoEdit; 55 (l) ©Mark Richards/PhotoEdit, (r) ©Tom Nebbia/Corbis; 56 (t) ©AFP/Corbis, (b) ©Corbis Sygma; 57 (c) ©Artville; (r) ©Alaska Stock Images; (b) ©PhotoDisc, Inc.; 58 ©Artville; 60 (b) ©Corbis; 67 ©PhotoDisc, Inc.; 68 ©Image Club; 69 (t) ©Robb Gregg Studios, (b) ©PhotoDisc, Inc.; 70 ©Robb Gregg Studios; 71 (t) ©Robb Gregg Studios, (b) ©Robb Gregg Studios; 72 ©PhotoDisc; 81 ©Corbis; 82 (t) ©David Young-Wolff/PhotoEdit, (c) ©PhotoDisc, Inc., (b) ©Map Resources; 83 (t) ©Comstock, (c) ©PhotoDisc, Inc.; 84 (t) ©PhotoDisc, Inc.; (c) ©PhotoDisc, Inc.; (b) ©Map Resources; 85 (t) ©George D. Lepp/Corbis, (c) ©Comstock, (b) ©Map Resources; 86 ©MetaCreations/Kai Power Photos; 95 ©Bettmann/Corbis; 96 ©Bettmann/Corbis; 97 ©Digital Vision/Punch Stock; 98 ©FPG/Hulton Archive/Getty Images; 99 ©Holos/Taxi/Getty Images; 100 ©Bettmann/Corbis; 107 (c) ©Dewitt Jones/Corbis, (b) ©Dan Guravich/Corbis; 108 (bl) ©Wolfgang Kaehler/Corbis, (tl) ©Richard Cummins/Corbis, (tr) ©Michael & Patricia Fogden/Corbis, (br) ©George McCarthy/Corbis; 109 (t) ©Roy Morsch/Corbis, (c) ©PhotoDisc, Inc.; 110 ©MetaCreations/Kai Power Photos; 111 ©PhotoDisc, Inc.

Illustration Credits:
COVER: Joanne Frair (c) 02 Janice Skivington-Wood, (b) Joanne Frair; 03 (t) Joe Boddy, (c) Michelle Dorenkamp, (b) Anni Matsick; 05–10 Janice Skivington-Wood; 19–24 Judith Pfeiffer; 33–38 Sally Springer; 47–52 N. Jo Tufts; 60 (t) N. Jo Tufts; 61–66 Michelle Dorenkamp; 75–80 Anni Matsick; 89–93 Joanne Frair; 103–106 Joe Boddy.

GETTING READY

LESSON 1 FICTION

Mack's Snack

Jesse and Robbie get a "snack attack" and want something to eat. Will they be able to follow their noses to the best snack?

Think About Fiction

Fiction is a made-up story. It is not true. Some fiction is about people who could be real. This is called **realistic fiction**. Think about realistic stories you have read that are made up.

Predict

Look at the title and pictures in the story. Two boys want a snack. What snacks do you think the boys might eat? Draw what you think Mack's snack is.

READING FICTION

STRATEGIES

Make Connections
Question
Make Inferences
Draw Conclusions

Mack's Snack

Make Connections
Think about what you might do to solve the problem that the character has.

I would ask my big sister to fix a snack for me.

What do you do when you are hungry?

"I'm hungry," Jesse said. "I want a snack."

"Me, too," Robbie said. "Amanda's mom is making cookies. We could ask her for one."

"How do you know she's making cookies?" Jesse asked.

"I can smell it. Can't you?" Robbie asked. "I would like a nice, hot cookie."

snack a food eaten between meals

"A cookie is good," Jesse said. "But popcorn is better. And I can smell it **popping** right now."

"I like popcorn, too," Robbie said. "Ms. Flores makes it when she watches the baseball game."

"We could visit her," said Jesse. "She will share some popcorn with us. What do you think?"

Question

Ask yourself questions about things you don't understand in a story. Reread or read ahead to find an answer.

I wonder, why didn't Jesse want a cookie? I think the smell of popcorn changed his mind.

Write another question you have about the story so far.

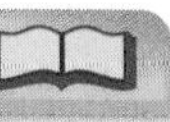

popping opening with a loud sound

Make Inferences
Sometimes the author doesn't tell you everything. Use what you have read and what you know to figure out something.

I know pizza comes in a large, flat box and smells good. I think Mack has a pizza!

Write which snack you think the boys like best.

The boys got up to go inside. Just then Mack walked by. He was coming home from his job at the factory. He carried a large, flat box.

"Do you smell what I smell?" Robbie asked.

"Yes, I do," Jesse said. "And it's better than popcorn."

"Hello, boys," Mack said. "Would you like to join me for a snack? I can't eat all of this by myself."

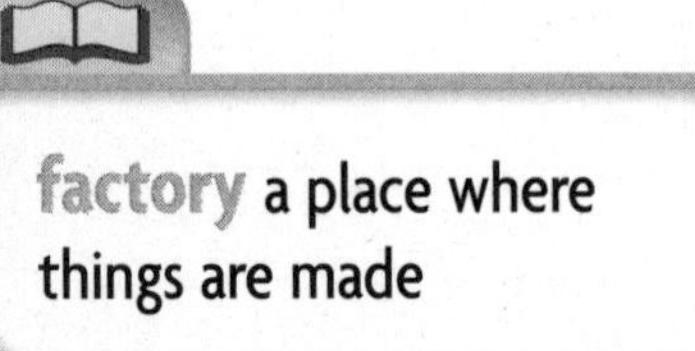

factory a place where things are made

"Thanks for the pizza, Mack," Robbie said. "It's good!"

"This is the best snack, Mack!" Jesse said. "Three cheers for Mack's pizza snack!"

Draw Conclusions
An author doesn't always tell you how characters feel. Think about what characters do or say to figure out how they feel.

Robbie says, "Thanks for the pizza." I think he is happy.

What else do the boys say and do to show how they feel?

Parts of a Story

Think about what happened in "Mack's Snack." Who are the characters? What is the problem? How is it solved? Fill in the story map.

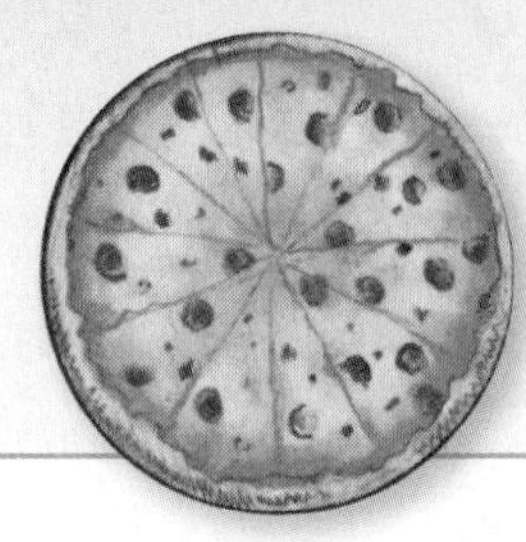

Characters

Jesse, Robbie, Mack

Problem

____

Events

1. Robbie smelled cookies baking.
2. Jesse smelled ______________________.
3. ______________________

Solution

____

Share

Use what you wrote in the boxes to retell the story to a friend.

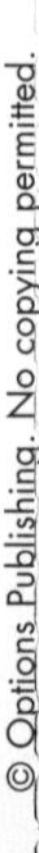

Food for a King and Queen

Did you know that a food you probably eat was made for a king and queen? Read the article to find out how that came to be.

Think About Nonfiction

Nonfiction is about real people and facts. We can read nonfiction in magazines. Sometimes **magazine articles** have headings that give clues about what you will read. Headings are like titles for the different parts in a magazine. Think about magazines you have seen or read. Write the title of one below.

____

____

Predict

Look at the article. Read the title and look at the pictures. Read the headings in the article. What do you think the magazine article is about? Write one idea on the lines below.

____

____

____

____

____

____

____

READING **NONFICTION**

STRATEGIES

Question
Understand Genre
Draw Conclusions

Food for a King and Queen

Question
Ask yourself questions as you read. This will help you learn more.

Why is a pizza thick or thin? Maybe the article will tell me.

Write another question you have.

____

____

____

____

You can top it. You can stuff it. You can make it thick or thin. What is it? It's pizza!

Many years ago, people ate flat, round bread. People bought it from a street **vendor**. But it wasn't the pizza we think of today. Where did one of the world's favorite foods come from?

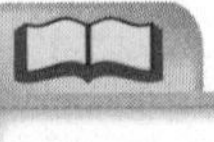

vendor a person who sells things

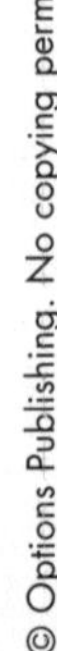

A Red, White, and Green Pizza

One day in 1889, the king and queen of Italy went to Naples. A baker wanted to make a special lunch for them. He made a pizza.

The pizza was like the flag of Italy. It was red, white, and green. The baker used tomatoes for red. He used cheese for white. He used basil for green. The king and queen loved it.

Understand Genre
(magazine article)
When you read a magazine article, don't forget to read the headings. They tell what you will read about.

This heading tells me that someone made a red, white, and green pizza.

Look at the heading on page 14. Write what you think that part will be about.

____

____

____

____

____

basil leaves of a plant used in cooking
Naples a city in Italy

Draw Conclusions
Use clues in an article to figure out something.

I think a pizzeria is a restaurant. People get pizza at a pizzeria.

Why did pizza change when it came to America?

____

____

____

____

____

____

____

Pizza Comes to America

In 1905, pizza came to America. The first pizzeria was in New York. Today, people go to pizzerias all over the country to eat pizza.

People in America changed pizza. They make it thick and eat it with a fork. Or they make it thin and eat it with their hands. Some people like everything on their pizza. Others like it with just cheese.

Question
Ask yourself questions when you don't understand what you are reading. Reread or read ahead to find an answer.

Can I add broccoli to my pizza? It says you can put vegetables on a pizza, so the answer must be yes.

What do you like on your pizza?

____

____

____

____

____

Making Pizza Your Way

How do you make pizza? Pizza starts with flat, round bread **dough**. Then you add tomato sauce. If you like, you can add almost any kind of meat. You can put lots of vegetables on the pizza, too. Finally, top it with cheese and bake it.

Pizza is not just for kings and queens. It's for everybody. What do YOU like on your pizza?

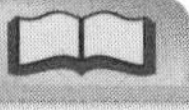

dough a mix of flour and water that is baked to make bread

Food for a King and Queen

Sequence

Think about how a pizza is made. You need to follow steps in a certain order. Fill in the boxes with the steps you would follow to make a pizza. Use the article to help you.

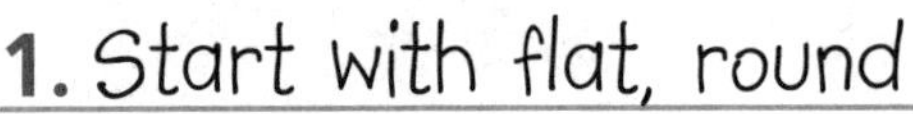

1. Start with flat, round bread dough.

2. Then, add _____.

3. If you like, add _____.

4. You can also add _____.

5. Finally, top it with _____ and bake it. Enjoy!

Share

Tell a friend or family member about the red, white, and green pizza. Then share how you would make your pizza.

Food for a King and Queen

Make Connections

Think about what you read in "Mack's Snack" and "Food for a King and Queen." Think about how the two selections connect to each other and to you.

1. Write two things you learned about pizza.

a. ______________________________

b. ______________________________

2. How is Mack's pizza like the flag of Italy?

____

____

3. Draw what you would like on your pizza.

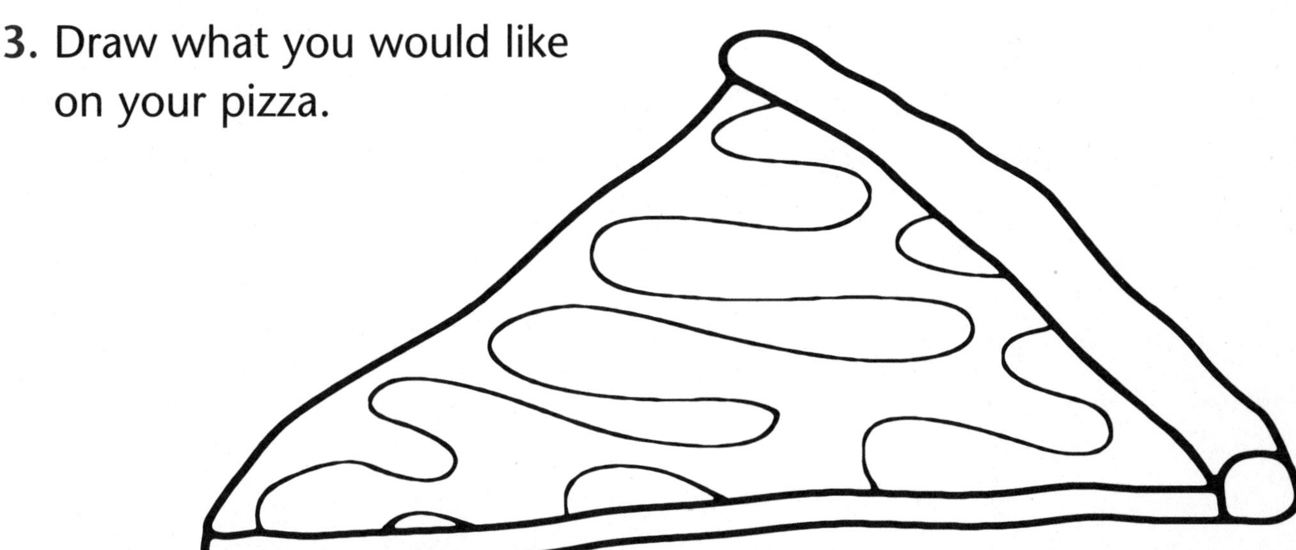

Write a Recipe

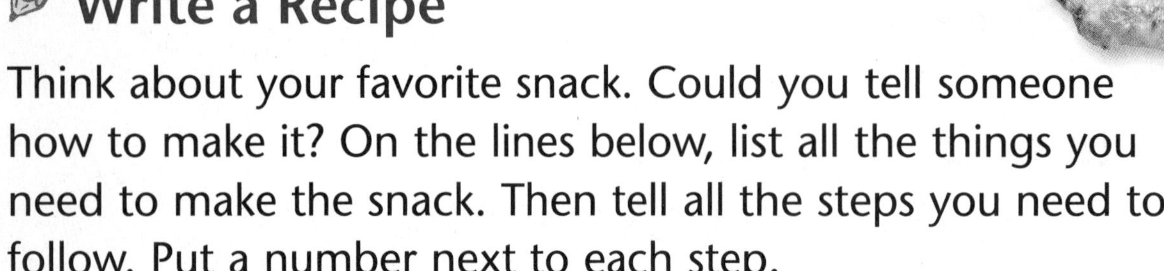

Think about your favorite snack. Could you tell someone how to make it? On the lines below, list all the things you need to make the snack. Then tell all the steps you need to follow. Put a number next to each step.

My Favorite Snack

Things That Are Needed:

Steps to Follow:

LESSON 2 FICTION

The Building Team

Paddy and Paws are old enough to help their parents build a dam. Can they work together as a team?

Think About Fiction

A **fiction** story is made up. It is not true. Some fiction stories are **fantasy**. Fantasy stories tell about things that could not really happen. In this fantasy story, the animals talk. Think about another fantasy story you have read. Write the title on the lines.

Predict

Look at the title and the pictures in the story. Two beavers are learning to help their parents. What are they learning to do?

STRATEGIES

Make Connections
Draw Conclusions
Question
Visualize

The Building Team

Make Connections
Think about how you would feel if you were one of the characters.

Paddy and Paws are happy to help their parents. I would be, too.

Tell how you feel when you help a grown-up.

The Beaver family is building a new home. This year, Paddy and Paws are old enough to help Mama and Papa Beaver build the dam.

"Let's see who can put the most logs on the dam," calls Paddy.

Paws shakes her head. "Mama says the dam has to be strong, not just big."

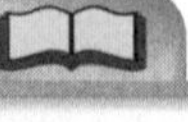

dam a wall that stops water

Paddy pulls many logs to the stream. "My side is going to be so tall," he says.

Paws packs her logs with mud. "My side is going to be as strong as can be," she says.

Draw Conclusions
Use what the characters say or do to learn about them.

The author doesn't say it, but I think Paddy and Paws are hard workers.

What are Paddy and Paws doing that could make you think they are hard workers?

stream a small river

Question

As you read, ask yourself questions about things you don't understand. Reread or read ahead for an answer.

Why aren't Paddy and Paws happy? I have to read this again to find the answer.

Circle the answer in the story. Write it below.

Paddy steps back to look at his work. "Do you see how tall my side is?" he asks.

"I see water coming through the dam," Paws says. "Look how strong my side is."

"I see water coming over the top," says Paddy.

Paddy and Paws are not happy. They do not know what to do.

Visualize
Use what you have read to make a picture in your mind.

Tell how the dam looks different now.

"If I give you some more logs," Paddy says, "then your side will be taller."

"Thank you," says Paws. "I can help you pack some mud. That will stop your leak." Paddy and Paws work together.

"That looks great!" says Mama Beaver. "I see a strong dam and a strong building team."

Sequence

Think about "The Building Team." What happens first? What happens next? Write the order of events on the chart below. The first two have been done for you.

The beavers are building a dam.

↓

Paddy wants to build a tall dam.

↓

Paws wants to ____________________.

↓

But the dam ____________________.

↓

____

Share

Use what you wrote in the chart to tell a friend about "The Building Team."

Busy as a Beaver

A pile of sticks and mud stops a stream. Who made that pile? Why is it in the middle of the stream?

Think About Nonfiction

Nonfiction writing is true. It has facts that teach you something. One kind of nonfiction is an **article** that gives information. Think about something you have read that is true. What did you learn?

Predict

Read the title of the article. Look at the pictures. Tell what you think the informational article is about.

Reading Nonfiction

STRATEGIES

Question
Understand Genre
Make Connections
Visualize

Busy as a Beaver

A huge pile of sticks, rocks, and mud stops a stream. Who did that? A beaver could have done it.

Beavers build dams. They build dams to make ponds. On land, beavers are slow. In the water, they are **champion** swimmers!

Question
Ask yourself questions as you read. Reread or read ahead to find the answers.

How do beavers build their dams? I'll read on to find out.

Write a question you have about beavers.

____

____

____

____

champion the best

Why Beavers Build

Beavers build homes in the water to protect themselves. A home in the water makes it easier for them to get food, too.

If a stream is not deep enough, beavers build a dam. The dam stops the water from moving. This makes a pond.

Once there is a pond, the beavers build a lodge, or home, in the middle. They get into the lodge from under the water.

Understand Genre
(informational article)
Headings are titles to each part in an article. Use headings to help you understand what you are reading.

The heading says "Why Beavers Build." In this part, I will learn why beavers build dams.

Look at the heading on page 28. What will the next part be about?

____

____

____

____

How Beavers Build

Beavers cut down trees with their sharp front teeth. A beaver can chew through a three-inch tree in about ten minutes.

To start a dam, beavers push the ends of some logs into the stream. The logs hold up other logs and sticks that the beavers bring. Beavers also add rocks and mud. They keep adding to the dam until it stops the water from flowing.

Make Connections

When you read, think about your own life and the things you know. This helps you understand the ideas.

I'll use my ruler to see what three inches looks like. This is how much a beaver can chew through.

Write two other things that are three inches long.

____

____

____

____

____

flowing moving along

Visualize
Use words in an article to make a picture in your mind.

I can picture a frozen pond because I read the words "winter" and "freeze."

What other picture do the words on this page help you "see"?

What words help you "see" it? Circle them in the article.

Beavers Keep Building

The water in the pond has to be just right for a beaver's lodge. If the water is too shallow, the pond will freeze in winter. If the water is too deep, it will go over the top of the lodge.

A beaver dam is never really done. Beavers add sticks or move them around. These animals have to stay "as busy as beavers" to keep a dam strong.

shallow not deep

Make Inferences

After you read an article, think about the facts. Use the facts from the article and what you know to answer the questions below.

Fact: Beavers have sharp teeth.
Would a beaver make a good pet? Why or why not?

____

____

Fact: Beavers are good swimmers.
Do you think beavers have strong legs? Why or why not?

____

____

Fact: Beavers use trees to build lodges and dams.
What tree parts might be in a beaver lodge or dam?

____

____

Share

Tell a friend or your family what you learned about beavers.

Make Connections

Think about "The Building Team" and "Busy as a Beaver." Think about how they are the same. Think about what you learned from both.

1. Think about the dams in the story and the article. How are they the same?

____

____

____

2. Think about the beavers in the story and the article. Tell one way they are the same and one way they are different.

Same	Different
____________________	____________________
____________________	____________________
____________________	____________________
____________________	____________________

Write Events in Order

Beavers do things in order when they build a dam. You do things in order, too. When you get ready for school, you do some things first and some things last. Tell what you do to get ready for school in the order you do it. For example: First, I eat breakfast. Then, I brush my teeth.

Getting Ready for School

First, I ______________________________

______________________________.

Then, I ______________________________

______________________________.

Next, I ______________________________

______________________________.

Finally, I ______________________________

______________________________.

LESSON 3 FICTION

The Visit

At first, Elisa does not like hospitals. Then something happens to change her mind.

Think About Fiction

"The Visit" is a **realistic fiction** story. It is a made-up story that seems real. What made-up stories have you read that seemed real? Write the title of one story on the lines below.

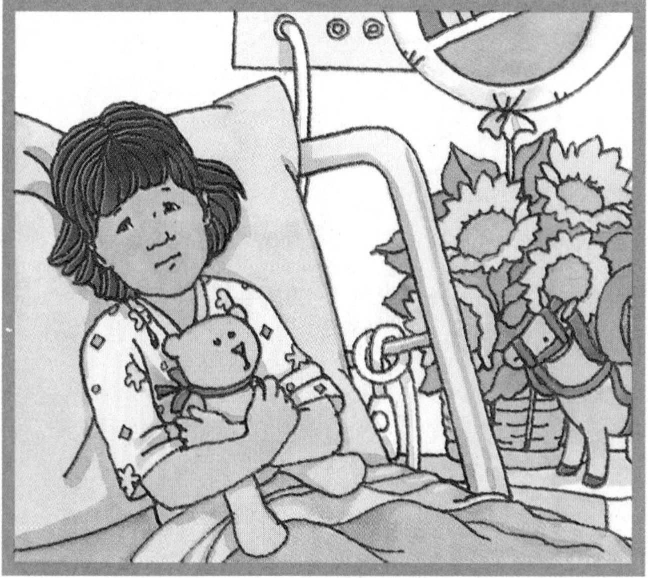

Predict

Look at the title and the pictures in the story. What do you think happens to change Elisa's mind about hospitals? Write a sentence.

READING **FICTION**

STRATEGIES

Make Connections
Question
Understand Genre
Draw Conclusions

The Visit

Make Connections
Think about how you might feel if you were one of the characters.

If I were in the hospital, I would miss my school friends.

How would you feel if you were Elisa?

Kim and Carlos were **nervous**. They had never been in a hospital. They were there to see their friend Elisa. She had an **operation** to help her walk better.

"Elisa was worried about being in the hospital," Kim said.

"I bet she doesn't like being here," said Carlos.

nervous afraid

operation something a doctor does to make a person feel well again

"How are you?" Kim asked in a soft voice.

"I'm much better than I thought I would be!" Elisa laughed.

"Really?" Carlos said with surprise.

"I am learning a lot here," answered Elisa.

Just then a man walked into Elisa's room. Carlos and Kim **gasped**. He had on all green clothes. There was a mask on his face. He wore a strange hat and had funny covers on his shoes.

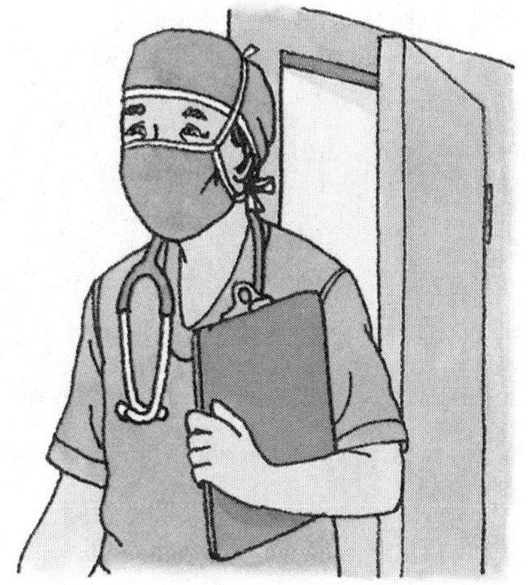

Question

Ask yourself questions about what is happening in the story. This helps you understand what you are reading.

I wonder, what is Elisa learning? Maybe she is learning what doctors do.

Write another question about this part of the story.

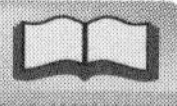

gasped took in a fast, sudden breath

Understand Genre
(realistic fiction)
Stories that are realistic fiction have people and places that could be real.

Real doctors wear funny clothes. Dr. Diaz could be a real doctor.

What other detail in the story could really happen?

"Don't be scared," Elisa said. "This is Dr. Diaz. He did my operation. His funny clothes cover him up so he does not spread germs."

Dr. Diaz told a joke. Everyone laughed.

Elisa asked, "Dr. Diaz, may I take my friends to the playroom?"

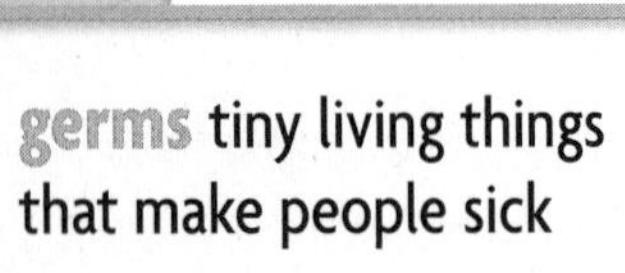

germs tiny living things that make people sick

In the playroom, there were many children. Elisa introduced some of them. "Dr. Diaz fixed Yuki's sore neck," she told them. "He took care of Gina's broken arm. He also made Rick's hand work better."

"This place isn't scary at all," Kim said.

"Dr. Diaz helps a lot of children," said Carlos.

"I want to help lots of people, too, said Elisa. I want to be a doctor when I grow up."

Draw Conclusions
Authors do not tell everything that happens. They give clues to help you figure it out.

It doesn't say, but I think Dr. Diaz is a good doctor because he helps everyone get better.

How do you know that Dr. Diaz is a good doctor?

introduced helped one person meet another person

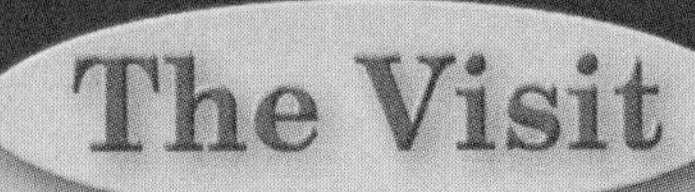

Cause and Effect

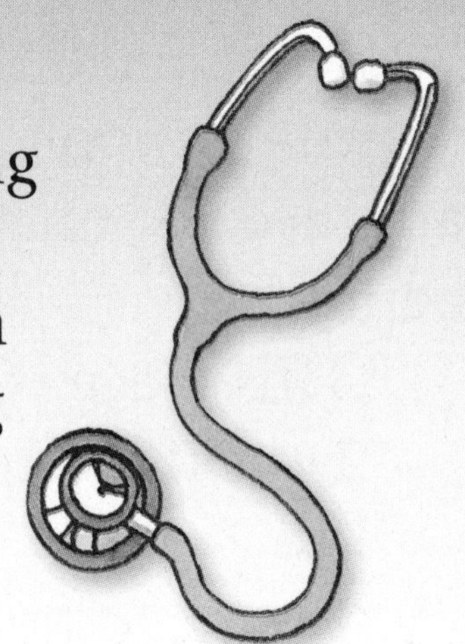

When something happens, it is because something else causes it to happen. In "The Visit," Elisa is in the hospital (the **effect**) because she is having an operation (the **cause**). Fill in the chart by writing the cause for each effect in "The Visit." The first one has been done for you.

Effect		Cause
Elisa has to be in a hospital	→	because she is having an operation.
Dr. Diaz does not spread germs	→	because his clothes ________________ ________________.
Elisa wants to be a doctor	→	because ________________ ________________.

Share

Use what you wrote to tell a friend about Elisa's stay in the hospital.

GETTING READY

Believe in Yourself

Ben's family is poor, but Ben has big dreams. Can he make his dreams come true by believing in himself?

Think About Nonfiction

Biography is one kind of **nonfiction**. A biography tells the true story of a person's life. Think about the stories you have read about people's lives. Write the title of one on the line.

Predict

Read the title. Look at the pictures. Write a sentence that tells what you think this biography is about.

READING NONFICTION

STRATEGIES

Understand Genre
Draw Conclusions
Make Connections
Question

Believe in Yourself

Understand Genre (biography)
Biographies tell about people and what they have done.

This biography starts by telling about Ben when he was a boy.

Write one thing you learned about Ben.

____

____

____

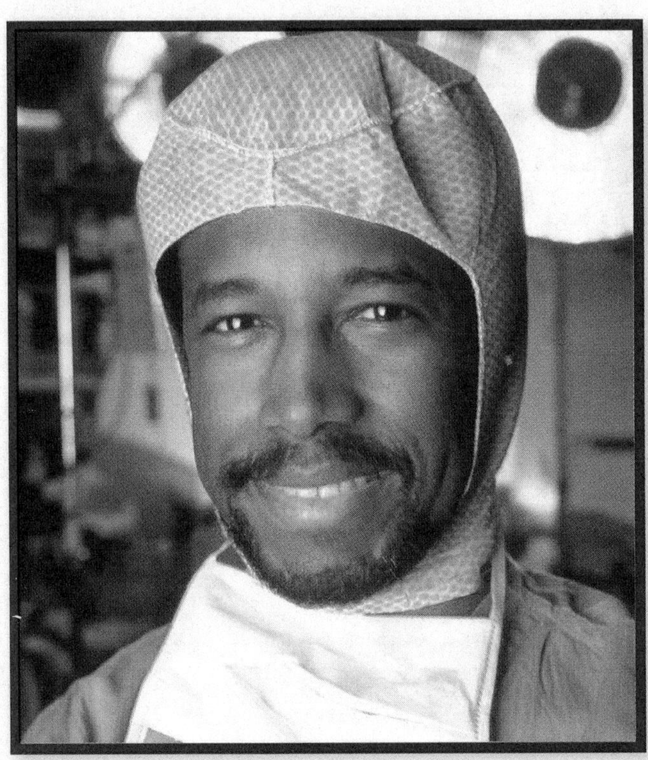

Ben Carson's mother told him, "Believe in yourself." That was hard to do. Ben's family was poor. Ben had a hard time at school. He had a terrible temper. But he took his mother's advice.

Ben's mother told him he could be anything he wanted to be. Ben wanted to be a doctor. How could Ben make this happen?

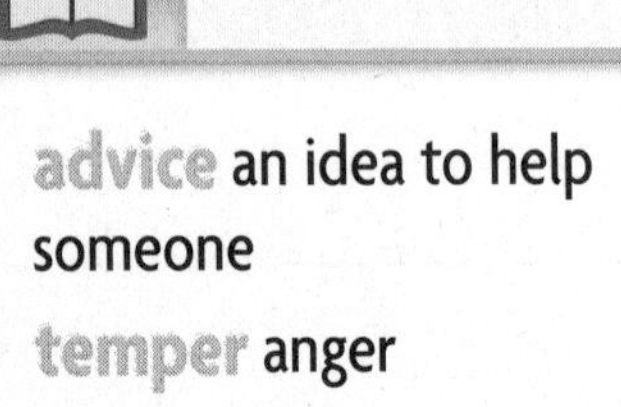

advice an idea to help someone

temper anger

Mrs. Carson made Ben turn off the TV. She made him read. At first, Ben was not happy. Later, he saw how much he was learning. Maybe he *could* become a doctor.

Ben became a good student. He got into **college**. The work was very hard. Ben studied from 6:00 in the morning until 11:00 at night.

Draw Conclusions
Authors don't always tell you everything. You have to use clues to figure things out.

At first, Ben did not do well in school. Later, he did well. Maybe he was not trying very hard at first.

What else can you tell about Ben when he was a student?

____

____

____

____

____

college a school after high school

Make Connections
Think about how you would feel if you were Ben. This helps you understand the person better.

I think Ben must feel thankful that he worked hard.

How else might Ben feel about his work?

____

____

____

____

____

Ben made his dream come true. He became a doctor. Now he is a brain **surgeon**. Ben works mostly with children.

Dr. Carson is not an **ordinary** doctor. Ben has found new ways to make people well. He has saved many children's lives. People from all over the world ask for his help.

ordinary usual, common
surgeon a doctor who operates on living things

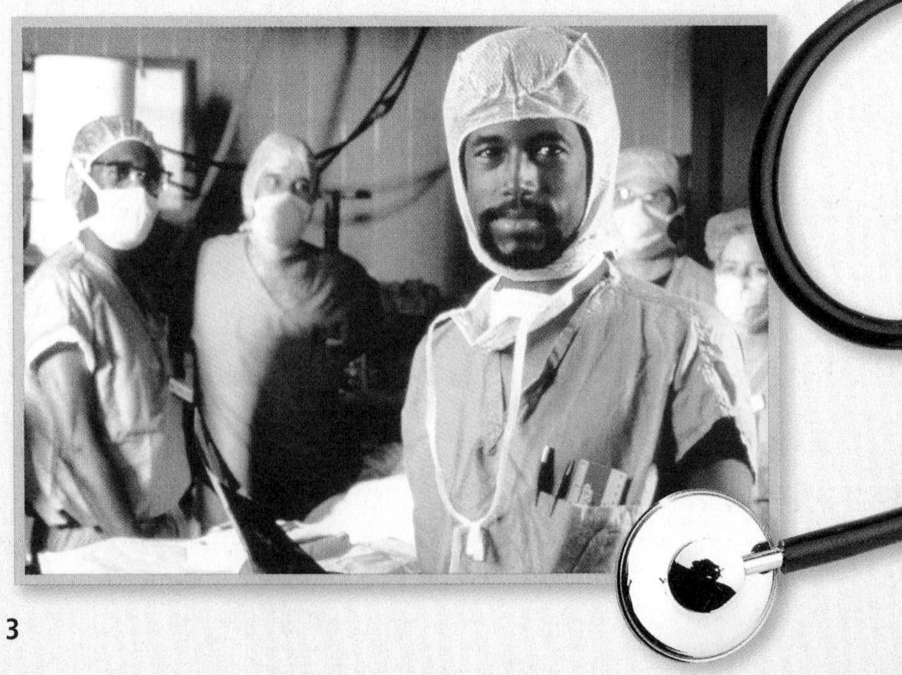

Many people ask Ben to share his ideas. He especially likes to talk to children.

Ben tells students the same thing his mother told him. He says, "Believe in yourself." He tells children to work hard. He tells them they can make their dreams come true.

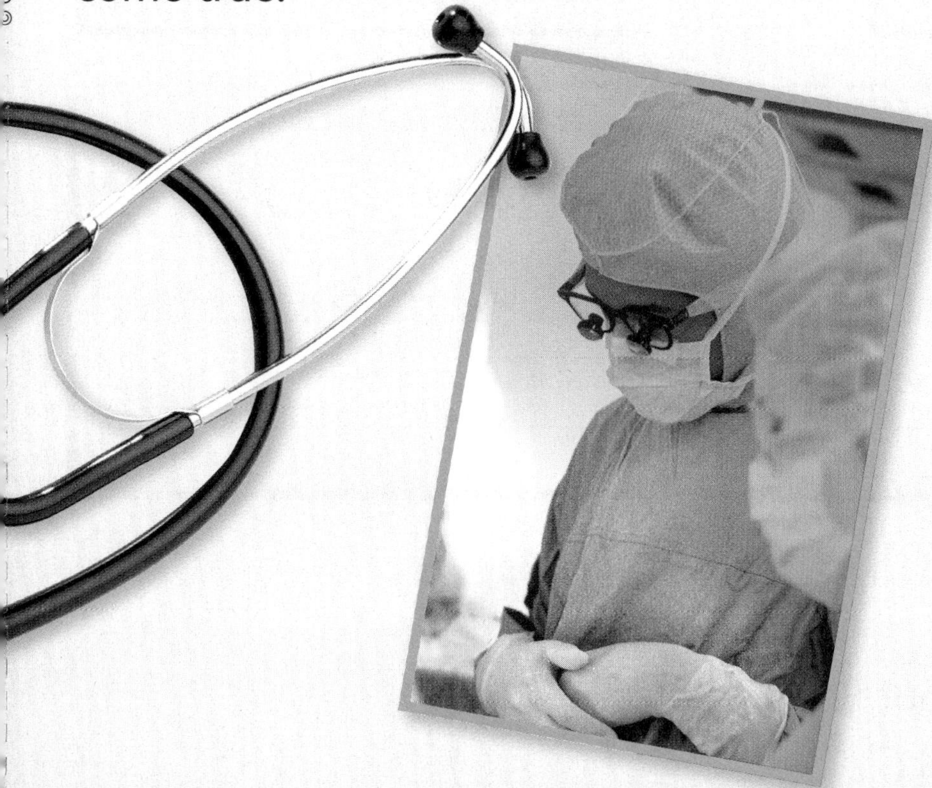

Question

Ask yourself questions about what you read in a biography. This will help you understand it better.

I wonder, what questions do children ask Ben? They might ask what else his mother told him.

Why does Ben like to talk to children?

____

____

____

____

____

____

especially very much

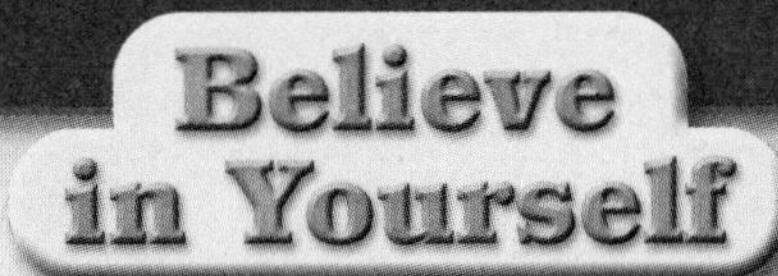

Main Idea and Details

The most important idea in Ben Carson's biography is called the **main idea**. Ideas that tell more about the main idea are called the **details**. Write about Ben's life in the chart below.

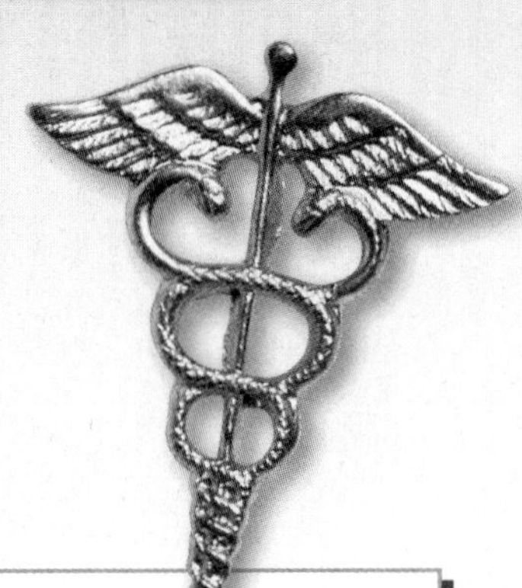

Main Idea:

Ben helps many children today because ______________________________

____.

Detail 1
At first, Ben had a hard time at school.

Detail 2
Ben's mother told him to

____

______________________________.

Detail 3
Ben started to ______________

____

______________________________.

Detail 4
Ben became a doctor who

______________________________.

Share

Tell someone at home about Ben Carson's life.

Believe in Yourself

Make Connections

Think about "The Visit" and "Believe in Yourself." Think about how the two selections connect to each other.

1. How are Dr. Diaz and Dr. Carson alike?

____

____

2. How are Dr. Diaz and Dr. Carson different?

____

____

____

3. What do you think Dr. Carson would think of "The Visit" if he read it? Why?

____

____

____

Write Advice

Think about the advice Ben's mother gave him. What advice would you give someone who wants to be a doctor? Write your idea. Then tell the reasons.

My advice is

.

This is important because

.

Junior Iditarod Jitters

Bo is excited and worried. Does he have what it takes to finish the big dog-sled race?

Think About Fiction

All **fiction** stories are made up. Sometimes authors put people and events in their stories that could be real. These stories are called **realistic fiction**.

Predict

Read the title and look at the pictures in the story. Bo is going on a long dog-sled race. Draw something that you think might happen.

READING **FICTION**

STRATEGIES

Draw Conclusions
Visualize
Question
Make Connections

Junior Iditarod Jitters

Draw Conclusions
Use clues from the story to help you figure out something.

I think Bo is scared because he jumps when his father comes up behind him.

Why does Bo have the jitters?

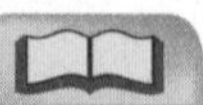

jitters scared and excited feelings

Junior Iditarod a dog-sled race for 14- to 17-year-olds

The dogs were quiet. "I wish I were that calm," Bo said to himself. He checked his lead dog's feet. They looked fine.

Bo's dad came up behind him. "Are you ready for the race?" he asked.

Bo jumped. "I think so."

Mr. Shelton looked at his son. "Do you have the **jitters**?"

Bo shook his head no. "I know I can do it," he said. Inside, he wasn't so sure. The **Junior Iditarod** race was two days of cold, snow, and ice. Could he make it?

Hours later, Bo still wasn't sure. His ten dogs raced across the snow. The sled nearly tipped over two times. Bo knew he had to trust the dogs.

Just after sunset, they reached the halfway point. Most of the teams were already there. The other drivers cheered as Bo pulled in.

Visualize
In your mind, try to picture what is happening. This helps you understand the story.

I can "see" Bo racing with his dogs on the white snow.

It is just after sunset. What does the sky look like?

trust depend on

Question

As you read, ask questions about things you don't understand. Reread or read ahead to find the answers.

Why does Bo have to feed his dogs right away? I reread the story and found out that the dogs come first.

Why does Jim Peters invite Bo to the campfire?

"How did it go?" Jim Peters asked.

"The dogs did well. But my face sure got cold," Bo said.

"Come over to the campfire," said Jim.

"I'll be over after I get food for the dogs," said Bo. He was so tired he could hardly walk. The dogs came first, though.

At sunrise, Bo and his dogs were ready. "Good luck, Jim," called Bo.

Jim looked sad. "My dogs got sick. I can't finish."

Bo knew there was nothing he could do. "Finish the race for both of us!" Jim said.

Bo grinned. "I will do it, Jim!"

Hours later, people cheered as the teams pulled into Settler's Bay. Bo's whole family was yelling. "Go, Bo!"

"I will never forget this day," Bo said to himself. "I finished the race."

Make Connections
Try to understand a character's feelings by thinking of how you would feel.

I feel bad when my friends have a problem, so Bo must feel sad about Jim's dogs.

If you have ever finished something difficult, you know how Bo feels. How would you feel if you were Bo and you finished the race?

Junior Iditarod Jitters

Parts of a Story

Think about the different parts of the story. Each part of the story tells about a different time. Some things happen in the beginning, some in the middle, and some in the end. In each box below, write another sentence that tells what happens in that part of "Junior Iditarod Jitters."

Beginning

Bo has the jitters.

____

Middle

Bo races through the snow.

____

End

Jim says his dogs are sick.

____

Share

Use the boxes to help you retell the story "Junior Iditarod Jitters" to a friend or family member.

Working Dogs

Many pet dogs spend their days sleeping. Working dogs don't have time to sleep a lot. How do they spend their days?

Think About Nonfiction

Nonfiction tells what is true about something. A **report** is nonfiction that gives information, or facts. In the report, "Working Dogs," each part begins with a heading that asks a question. What is a working dog?

____

____

____

Predict

Look through the report. Read the title and look at the pictures. Think about each question. Do you think you know the answer to a question? Write the question and your answer below.

____

____

____

____

____

____

READING **NONFICTION**

STRATEGIES

Make Connections
Understand Genre
Visualize
Make Inferences

Working Dogs

Make Connections
As you read, think about what you already know.

I know about guide dogs. I saw one helping someone cross the street.

What have you seen a working dog do in real life or on TV?

____

____

____

____

____

Have you ever heard someone say, "work like a dog"? Do you know any dogs that work? Some dogs have real jobs. These working dogs help people in many ways.

What kinds of dogs help people?

Different kinds of dogs are great for certain jobs. Labs make good helping dogs. Huskies are good for pulling sleds in snow. German Shepherds make good search dogs.

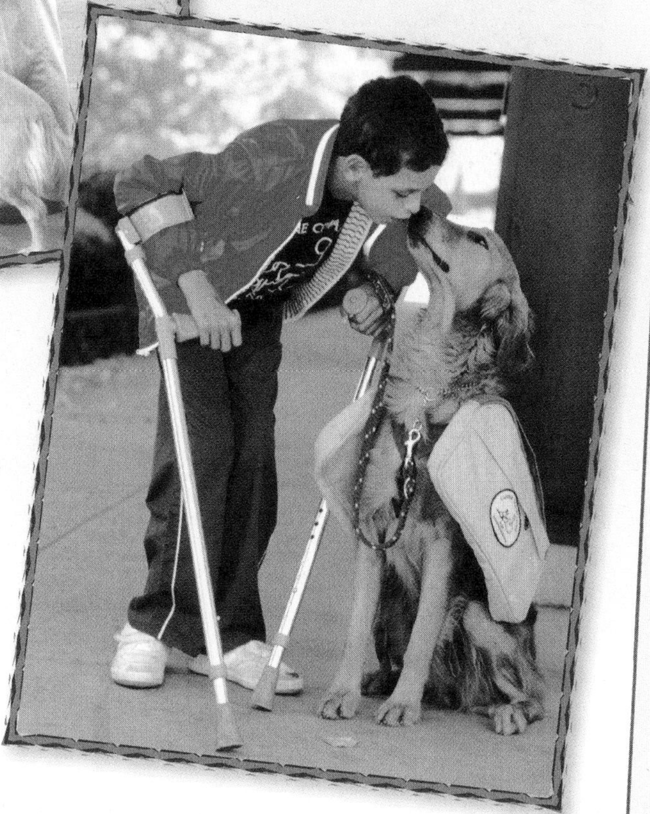

Understand Genre (report)

Reports give information. We learn from them. What does this part of the report tell about?

The heading, "What do guide dogs do?" tells me that this part is about what guide dogs do.

Look at the next page. What do you think you will learn about in that part?

What do guide dogs do?

Guide dogs get special training. Then they live with a person who is blind. Guide dogs stay with their owners at all times.

If the owner is at home, the guide dog is at home. If the owner goes out, the dog goes along. Guide dogs lead their owners across busy streets. They ride with them on buses and trains. They help their owners lead active lives.

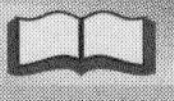

active able to move around

blind not able to see

Visualize

Making a picture in your mind of what you read will help you remember.

In my mind, I can "see" a rescue dog sniffing a pile and finding somebody who's trapped.

What do you "see" guide dogs doing on page 55? Draw it.

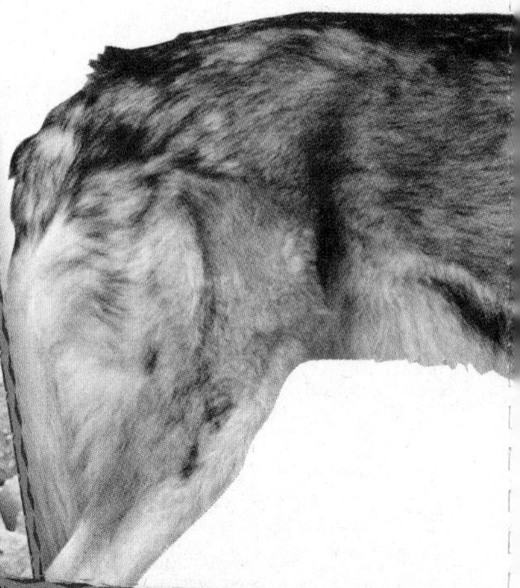

What are rescue dogs?

Sometimes people get trapped or lost. Search teams try to find them. A dog is often part of the team. The dog helps rescue, or save, people.

Rescue workers look for people when a building falls. Dogs join the search. They sniff for people who are trapped.

Why would you bring a dog on a search? Dogs have a great sense of smell. They can use their noses to find a person.

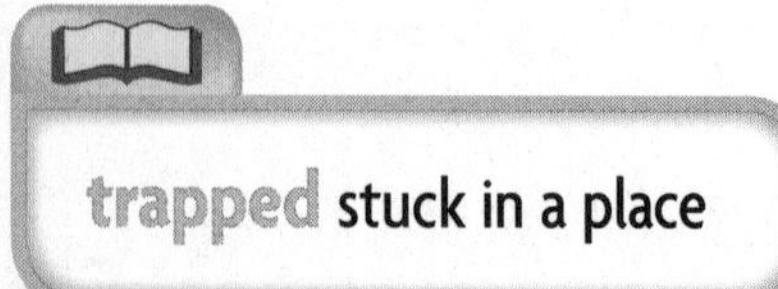

trapped stuck in a place

What are sled dogs?

Long ago, people of the Far North used dog sleds to go from place to place in the snow. Dogs helped these people live through the winter. Today, dog sleds are used for fun.

The Iditarod is Alaska's most famous dog-sled race. It is a thousand miles long. A shorter race, the Junior Iditarod, is for boys and girls from 14 to 17 years old. Both races test the **teamwork** between sled drivers and their dogs.

Dogs really CAN work!

Make Inferences
Authors do not always tell you everything. Find clues and use what you know to figure out something.

The author doesn't say how people in the Far North get around now. I read that dog sleds are used for fun. I think people probably use cars, trucks, and planes.

How old do you think the racers in the thousand-mile Iditarod are?

____

____

____

teamwork working together

Working Dogs

Main Idea

Each part of "Working Dogs" has a main idea. Main ideas give you the most important information. Finish writing a main idea for each part below. Tell how each kind of dog helps people.

What do guide dogs do?

Guide dogs stay with ______________________________

______________________________.

What do rescue dogs do?

Rescue dogs help search teams by ______________________________

______________________________.

What do sled dogs do?

Sled dogs used to help people go ______________________________.

Now, they ______________________________.

Share

Tell a friend or family member about dogs that work. Use the information in the boxes to help you.

Junior Iditarod Jitters

Make Connections

Think about how "Junior Iditarod Jitters" and "Working Dogs" connect to each other.

1. What information is the same in both "Junior Iditarod Jitters" and "Working Dogs"?

____

____

2. Teamwork is important for Bo and his dogs. Why is teamwork important for other people and their working dogs, too?

____

____

____

3. Tell one way the dogs in the story are different from the dogs in the report.

____

____

Write a Postcard

Pretend you are in Alaska to cheer for a friend in the Junior Iditarod race. Write a postcard to a friend or family member. Tell what you saw, how you felt, and what it was like to be there.

Dear ____________________,

____

____

____

____

____

Your friend,

____

Greetings from Alaska!

GETTING READY

LESSON 5 FICTION

The Best Holiday

Most years, Cam loves the Trung Thu holiday, but not this year. Why is Cam so upset?

Think About Fiction

"The Best Holiday" is a **realistic fiction** story. It is a made-up story that seems real. The characters do things that real people do. "The Best Holiday" takes place in another country. What story have you read that takes place in another country?

____

____

____

Predict

Read the title. Look at the pictures in the story. Write one thing you think happens on the holiday of Trung Thu.

____

____

____

____

____

____

____

____

STRATEGIES

Question
Visualize
Make Connections
Make Inferences

The Best Holiday

Question
Ask yourself questions as you read.

I wonder, what kind of mask will Cam's mother make?

Write a question you have so far.

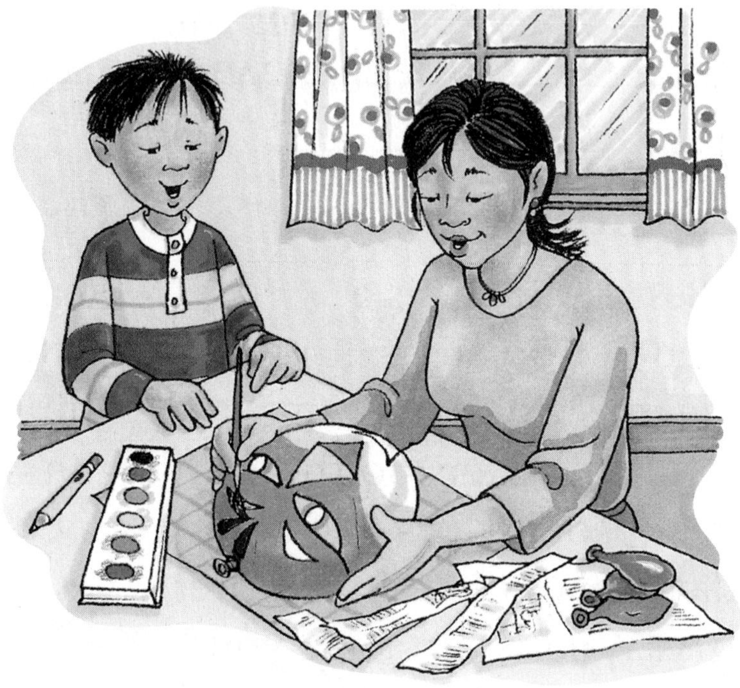

Cam was excited. The Vietnamese holiday of Trung Thu was coming. The Children's Festival! Cam loved eating moon cakes and marching in the parade. The best part, though, was wearing a mask. Last year, his parents took him to the store to pick out his favorite mask.

A few days ago, Cam saw Mom making something.

"What's that?" Cam asked.

"I'm making you a papier-mâché mask," Mom said. "We do not have extra money to buy a mask this year."

papier-mâché a mix of paper and paste

Trung Thu a holiday to honor the moon

Cam was very upset. "No one wears a homemade mask. Everyone will laugh at me," Cam said.

A few days later, on Trung Thu, Cam announced, "I am not going to the parade."

"Yes, you are. It will be fun!" said Dad.

"Here is your mask," said Mom.

"I will carry it," said Cam.

Visualize

As you read, make pictures in your mind. It will help you understand what is happening.

I can "see" Cam with a sad look on his face as he leaves for the parade.

How did Cam's parents look on their way to the parade?

announced said, told

homemade made at home, not in a factory

Make Connections
When you read a story, think about your own life. What does the story remind you of?

I remember the time I wanted to hide because I had a bad haircut. I felt like Cam probably feels.

What other holiday does Trung Thu remind you of? Why?

Cam hid his mask behind his back. He did not talk to his friends. Soon it was time for the parade.

"Put on your mask," said Dad.

Cam could not **disobey** his father. He put on the mask. Cam got in line behind a tall boy. "Maybe no one will know it's me," he thought.

Cam felt like people were staring at him during the parade. Some pointed at his mask. He wanted to **disappear**.

disappear to go out of sight
disobey to not do what you are told

Finally, the parade was over. Cam quickly took off his mask. A friend called to Cam. "Hey, Cam! Everyone is talking about your mask," she said.

"I know," mumbled Cam.

"It was the best! It was the brightest mask in the parade. We all want masks like yours next year."

Cam grinned and looked up at Mom.

"Thanks," he said, as he put his mask on again. Mom grinned back.

Make Inferences
Use clues in a story and what you know to figure out something.

When Cam said, "I know," he probably thought people were making fun of his mask.

Where do you think the other children got their masks?

finally at last
mumbled said in a low voice

Understand Characters

Think about the different feelings Cam had in the story. Think about why he felt like he did. Fill out the web to tell about his feelings and why he feels that way.

Cam

In the **beginning** of the story, Cam is **excited** because Trung Thu was coming.

In the **middle** of the story, Cam is **upset** because he does not

____

____

____

______________________.

Finally, in the **end**, Cam is

____

because ______________

____

____

______________________.

Share

Use what you wrote to tell a friend how Cam felt about his mask.

Making a Mask

It is fun to pretend to be another person or an animal. A mask can help you pretend. Find out how to make one.

Think About Nonfiction

Sometimes **nonfiction** articles tell you how to do something. They are called **"how-to" articles**. They tell you the steps to take and the things to use. Write one thing you know how to do.

Predict

Look at the pictures in "Making a Mask." Draw a picture of a mask you would like to make.

STRATEGIES

Understand Genre
Make Inferences
Visualize
Make Connections

Making a Mask

Understand Genre
(how-to article)
Most how-to articles start with a list of things you need. It is important to look at the list before you start.

The list helps me know what I need to get.

What else does the list tell you?

____

____

____

oval shaped like an egg

People all over the world use masks. They wear masks for fun, for special events, and in plays. People have been making and wearing masks for thousands of years.

Make your own papier-mâché mask using these things.

You will need:

newspaper
1/2 cup flour
1 teaspoon salt
1/2 cup water
a bowl
a spoon
round or oval balloon
safety scissors
a marker
paints
string or yarn

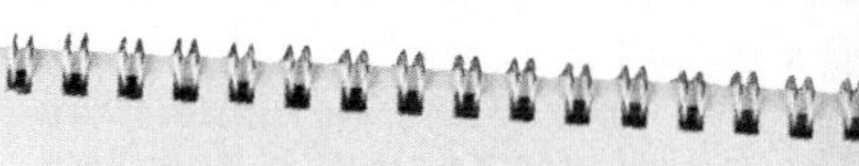

Make Inferences
How-to articles tell you what steps to take. Your project will turn out better if you figure out why a step is done a certain way.

The balloon has to be as big as your head because the mask has to fit your head.

Why do I have to pour the water slowly?

____

____

____

____

____

Follow these steps:

1. Prepare a table where you will work. Cover it with newspaper.
2. Tear other newspaper into strips that are one inch wide and one foot long. Tear about 40 strips.
3. Put the flour and salt into a bowl. Slowly pour in the water. Stir to make a thick, smooth paste.
4. Blow up a balloon until it is as big as your head. Tie the end.
5. Dip a strip of newspaper in the paste. Wipe off the extra paste with your fingers.

prepare to get ready

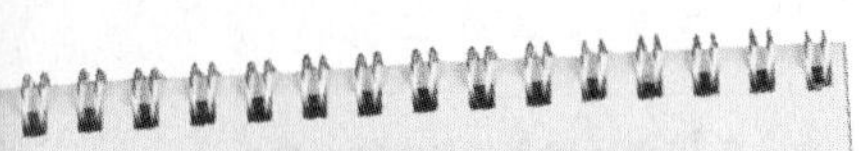

Visualize
Picture how each step should look. This will help you follow them.

I think after I do step 6, half of the balloon will be covered with paper. It will look like bandages covering a balloon.

How will the mask look after step 10?

6. Place the strip on the balloon from top to bottom. Cover half of the balloon with strips.
7. Then put a layer of strips on the balloon from side to side.
8. Repeat steps 5, 6, and 7.
9. Let it dry for three days. Then get the mask off by cutting a hole in the balloon. Throw out the balloon.
10. Cut the edges of the mask with safety scissors to make them even.

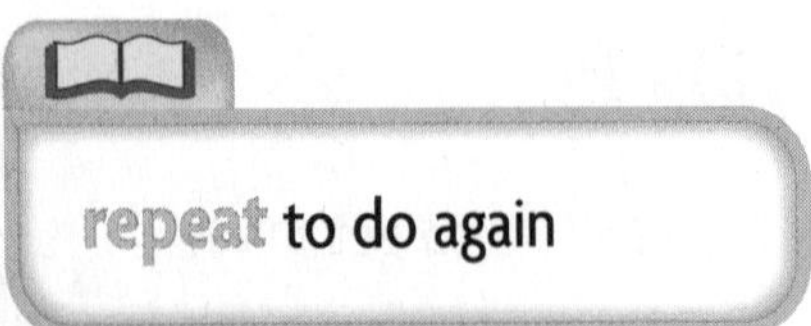

repeat to do again

11. Draw lines for your eyes, mouth, and nose on the mask. Ask an adult to cut out holes where the lines are. Also, have a tiny hole cut on each side just above where your ears will be.
12. Paint a **human** or animal face or a bright **design** on the mask. Let the paint dry.
13. Tie string or yarn through the holes on the sides of the mask. This will hold the mask onto your head.

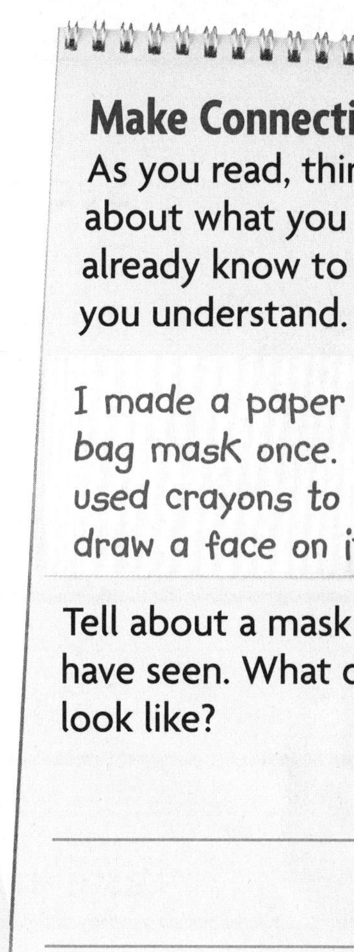

Make Connections
As you read, think about what you already know to help you understand.

I made a paper bag mask once. I used crayons to draw a face on it.

Tell about a mask you have seen. What did it look like?

____

____

____

____

____

____

design picture
human person

Sequence

Think about how to make a mask. Number the steps to show the correct order. The first and last steps have been done for you.

________ Tear paper into strips.

___7___ Paint the mask.

________ Paste the strips onto the balloon.

___1___ Gather the things you need.

________ Let it dry for three days.

________ Blow up a balloon.

________ Pop the balloon.

Share

Tell someone at home how to make a mask. Then, make one together.

Make Connections

Think about how "The Best Holiday" and "Making a Mask" connect to each other.

1. Who in "The Best Holiday" could use the steps in "Making a Mask" next year? Tell why.

____

____

____

2. How are the masks in the story and the article the same?

____

____

____

3. Think about making a mask. Could Cam's mother have made his mask on the day of the parade? Why or why not?

____

____

Write a How-to Article

Think about something you know how to make or do. It can be a food, a game, or a gift. First, write a list of things you need. Then write the steps in the order they should be done.

Title: How to

What You Need:

Steps to take: 1.

GETTING READY

LESSON 6 FICTION

Grandpa's Garden

Dina is shy because she is in a new place. Can a visit to Grandpa's garden make her feel more at home?

Think About Fiction

Fiction stories are made-up. Some **fiction stories** are about people and places that seem real. This is called **realistic fiction.** Think about other realistic stories you have read.

Predict

Read the title. Look at the pictures in "Grandpa's Garden." What kinds of plants does Grandpa have in his garden? Draw a picture of what grows in a garden.

STRATEGIES

Question
Understand Genre
Draw Conclusions
Make Connections

Grandpa's Garden

Question
Remember to ask yourself questions about things you do not understand in a story. Reread or read ahead to find the answers.

What country is Dina from? Read ahead to find the answer. Write it on the lines below. Then write a question you have.

Miguel and Sonia were visiting their grandfather. "Grandpa! Where are you?" they called.

"I'm out here in the garden," said Grandpa.

"Come meet our new friend," Sonia said. She smiled at Dina, who had just moved in next door to them.

Dina was too shy to smile back. Dina and her family were from another country.

Understand Genre
(realistic fiction)
Realistic fiction has details that make the story seem real.

Write something else that makes this story seem real.

Sonia took Dina to meet Grandpa. "I'm glad you could come, Dina," he said. Dina just nodded.

"What are these?" Miguel asked. He pointed to some little yellow flowers.

"Those flowers will become tomatoes," said Grandpa. "Did you know that tomatoes come from South America?"

"Just like our family!" said Sonia.

Draw Conclusions
An author doesn't always tell you everything. Use what you have learned about some plants to tell more about them.

What can you tell about many plants that are in gardens?

"These potatoes are from South America, too," said Grandpa. He pointed to the potato plants next to the tulips.

"Are tulips from South America, too?" asked Sonia.

"No, they come from a place called Turkey."

Dina grinned. "That's near Greece, where *my* family comes from."

Dina liked the garden and how nice Grandpa was, so she no longer felt shy. "Is everything in your garden from another place?" she asked.

Grandpa laughed. "No, but even the plants from other places are at home here now."

"Just like us!" said Sonia and Dina together.

Make Connections
As you read, think about when you have had the same feelings as one of the characters.

I feel shy sometimes. It feels good when I get to know people. Then I don't feel so shy.

What makes you feel less shy?

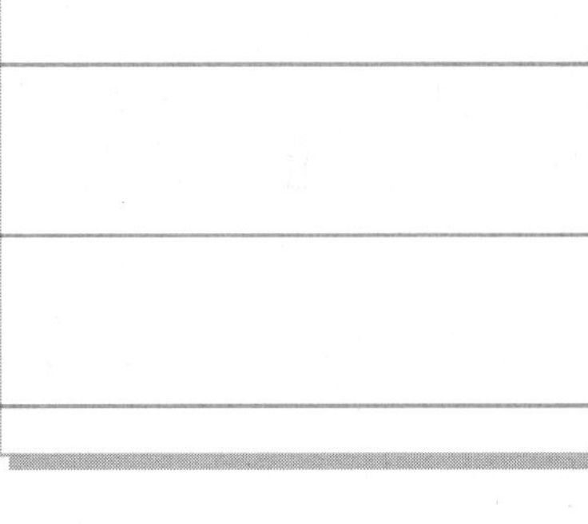

Grandpa's Garden

Parts of a Story

Think about "Grandpa's Garden." Who are the characters? What is the problem? What happens in the end? Fill in the chart to tell about "Grandpa's Garden."

Grandpa's Garden

The characters are ______________________________

____.

The problem is ________________________________

____.

Two things that happen are ______________________

____

____.

In the end, ___________________________________

____.

Share

Use what you wrote in the boxes to retell the story, "Grandpa's Garden," to a friend.

GETTING READY

Plants from Around the World

The people around us came from many different places in the world. Did you know that plants did, too?

Think About Nonfiction

Nonfiction has facts about real people, things, and events. A **report** gives facts about a topic. What is one thing a report could be about?

Predict

Read the title and look at the pictures in the report. What do you think you will read about? Write one idea on the lines below.

STRATEGIES

Visualize
Draw Conclusions
Understand Genre
Question

Plants from Around the World

Visualize
Authors use words to help you "see" what is happening.

I can "see" the plants growing in the mountains.

What else can you "see" in your mind?

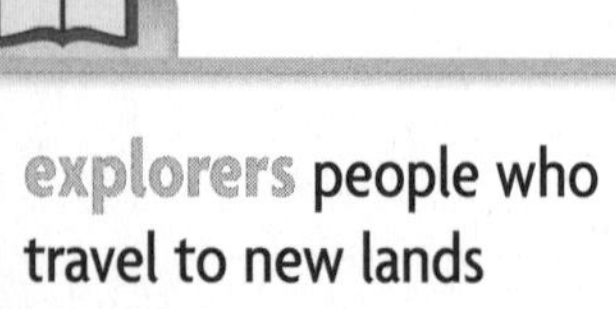

explorers people who travel to new lands

Many plants we see every day came from far away. Some of them have interesting stories.

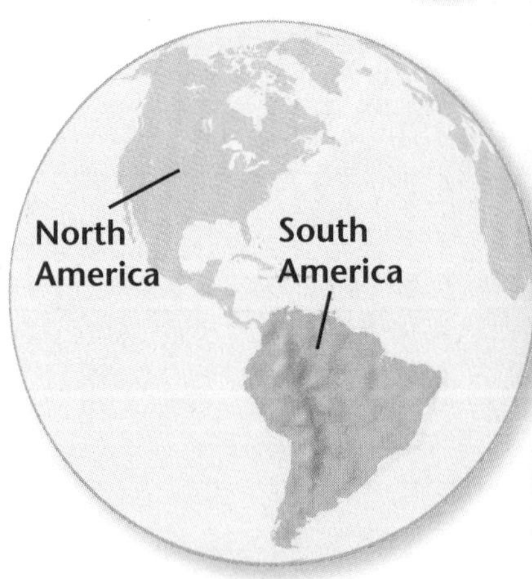

From South America

Tomatoes first grew in the mountains of South America. Hundreds of years ago, **explorers** carried the seeds or plants to Europe. There, some people ate the tomatoes. Other people thought the tomatoes would make them sick. In England, tomatoes were grown only in flower gardens.

Egypt

From Egypt

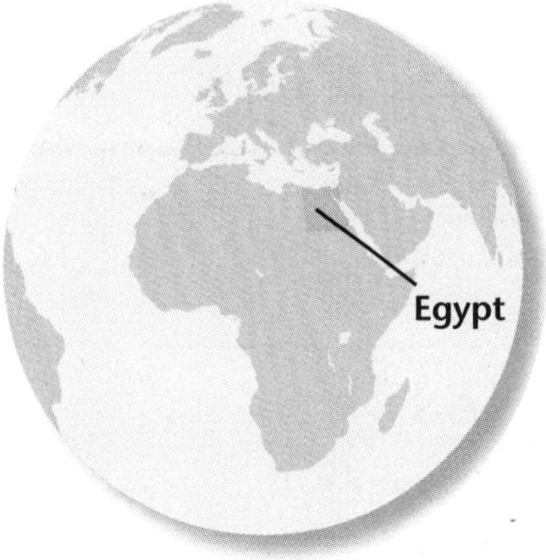

Rulers of Egypt ate carrots thousands of years ago. They weren't orange, though. Carrots were white, purple, red, yellow, green, and black!

Traders carried the seeds to other countries. Some people used carrots as medicine. English people really liked carrots. When the first English people came to North America, they brought carrot seeds with them.

Question

As you read, ask yourself questions about things you don't understand. Use what you know to answer them.

I wonder, why did people use carrots as medicine? They must have thought that carrots made them feel better.

Write a question you have about this part of the report. Ask a friend to answer it.

____

____

____

____

medicine something to help sick people get well

rulers people who run countries

Details

Think about what you learned from this report. Write two facts about each plant in the boxes. Look back in the report for ideas.

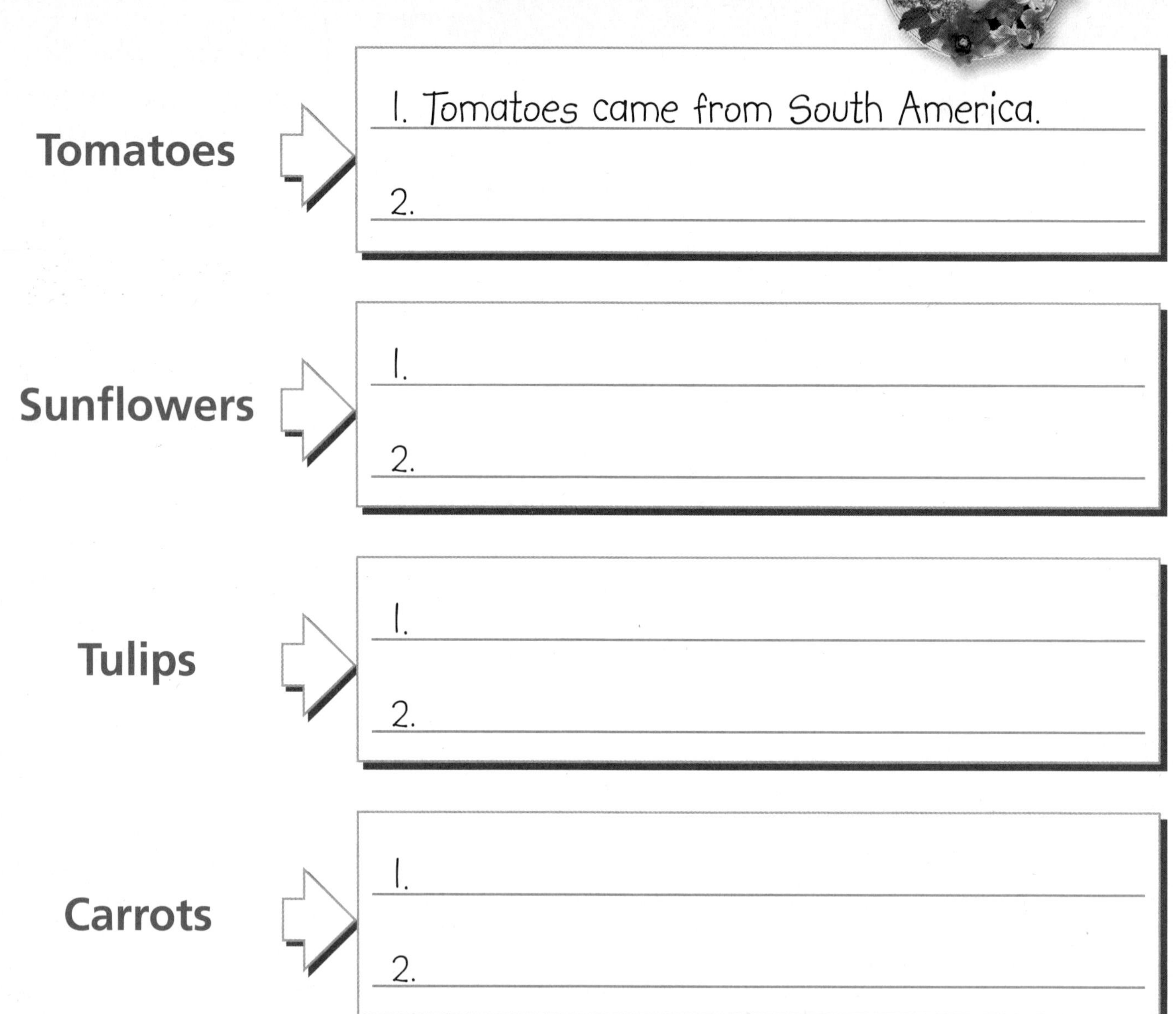

Share

Tell a friend or family member about one of the plants in the report. Draw a picture of that plant.

Make Connections

Think about "Grandpa's Garden" and "Plants from Around the World." Think about how the two selections connect to each other and to you.

1. Tell how "Grandpa's Garden" and "Plants from Around the World" are the same.

____

____

2. Which fact about tomatoes is in both selections?

____

____

3. Think about all the plants you read about. Which ones would you grow if you had a garden of your own? Tell why.

____

____

____

Write a Diary Entry

Imagine that you are Sonia in "Grandpa's Garden." Write a diary entry for your visit to Grandpa's. Write what you saw, what you did, and how you felt about your visit.

Date:

Dear Diary,

LESSON 7 FICTION

Michael's Big News

Michael's parents have bought their first car. Why is this such big news?

Think About Fiction

The **fiction** story you are about to read is in the form of a letter. The letter is **historical fiction**. Historical fiction is a made-up story about something that could have happened in the past, during a time in history. Think about an historical story you have read. Write the title below.

Predict

Read the title and the introduction to the story. Look at the pictures. What do you think Michael wrote about in his letter? Write one idea below.

READING **FICTION**

STRATEGIES

Draw Conclusions
Understand Genre
Visualize
Make Predictions

Michael's Big News

Draw Conclusions
Use what you have read to figure out things that are not in the letter.

Michael asks questions. I think he has been to the farm before.

Which clues tell that Michael has been to the farm?

May 1, 1915
Detroit, Michigan

Dear Grandma and Grandpa,

Are you both doing well? I miss you very much. How are the cows and the chickens? Did Bessie have her calf yet? I can't wait to see it!

Things are good here in Detroit. I have been learning a lot in school this year. I love math, and my writing is getting better. I have big news to tell you. I won a spelling bee! At first I was so afraid to stand in front of the class. But, I worked hard, and I won!

calf a young cow

The biggest news is that Mother and Father bought an automobile! It's a Model T. It has four doors and is shiny black. The space above the doors is open, but the top is covered. The top is soft. It keeps the sun off of us. The wheels are smaller than the ones on your buggy.

I think I would like to fix cars when I grow up. Father and I looked under the hood of the Model T today. He told me about the different parts. I liked learning about how the car works.

Understand Genre
(historical fiction)
Look for clues that tell you the events took place in the past.

Our car is different from the car Michael writes about.

Write one clue that shows the events took place in the past.

automobile car

buggy a wagon that is pulled by a horse

hood a cover over the front of a car

Visualize
As you read, make pictures in your mind.

I can "see" mother looking scared.

Write a detail from the story that helps you "see" the car ride in your mind.

Last Sunday Father drove us around town. He watched the road in front of him. Mother sat next to him and watched the road, too. I think she was scared Father might drive us into a **ditch**!

I sat in the back with my best friend Douglas. We had fun counting how many horses and buggies we passed on the road. Sometimes the wind blew our hair around. Some dust even got into the car. The ride was bumpy, loud, and fun. I'm glad Dad let Douglas come with us on the ride.

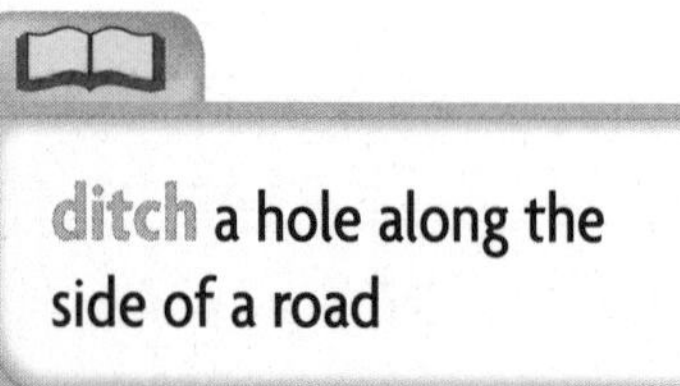

ditch a hole along the side of a road

Are you ready for some more big news? We are coming for a visit. Mother said we will drive our Model T to the farm! We will leave after school closes for the summer. Father says the trip will take a few days. He thinks the car may break down and need to be **repaired**.

I can't wait for the trip. I'm counting the days until we leave. Tell the calf I can't wait to pet her.

See you soon,
Michael

Make Predictions
As you read, think about what might happen next in the story.

Michael seems excited about the trip.

Write one thing you think might happen on the trip.

repaired fixed

Character

You can learn about Michael from his letter. Think about the things he wrote. Look at the chart. Read what Michael is like. Then finish each sentence with an example from the letter.

What Michael Is Like	How You Know
1. Michael is a good student	because ______________________ ______________________.
2. Michael likes his best friend Douglas	because ______________________ ______________________.
3. Michael loves his grandparents	because ______________________ ______________________.

Share

Tell a friend or family member what you learned about a Model T.

GETTING READY

Take a Drive THROUGH TIME

Cars have changed a lot over the years. They are different in many ways. Why have cars changed?

Think About Nonfiction

Nonfiction is about real people, things, and events. **Informational articles** give facts and details about real people, things, and events. They can help you learn about something new. Think about an informational article you have read. What was it about?

Predict

Read the title and the headings in the article. Look at the photos. Write one idea you think you will learn about cars.

STRATEGIES

Make Predictions
Make Connections
Make Inferences
Question

Take a Drive THROUGH TIME

Make Predictions
Make a prediction to think more about an idea.

I looked at the photos. I can see how early cars and today's cars are different.

Write what you think cars will be like in the future.

____

____

____

____

Cars were first made just over 100 years ago. Some of these cars were electric. They ran on batteries. Some of these cars ran on gasoline. Other cars ran on steam from boiling water! By 1915, most cars used **gasoline**, just like today.

Back then, a lot of people did not own cars. The Model T was the car that some people had. It was different from the cars that people drive today.

gasoline liquid used to run some machines

Make Connections As you read, think about what you already know.

I'll think about the cars I see and ride in every day.

Tell about a car you have been in. What did it look like?

One Car For All

The Model T came only in black. This is because it was made in a fast way. Many workers put together many parts. The parts were the same color, so all the cars looked the same.

Cars are still made this way today. But now there are more car companies. They make many **styles** of cars. People can buy cars in the shapes, sizes, and colors they like best.

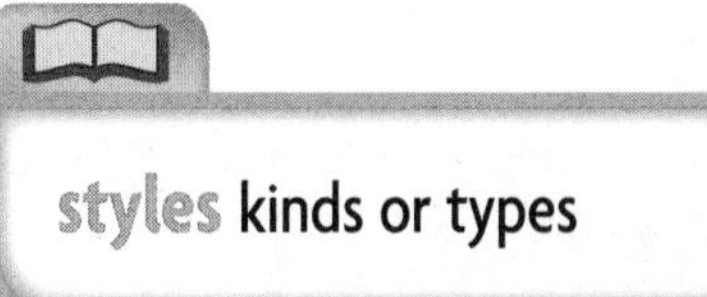

styles kinds or types

Make Inferences
Use what you have read and what you know to figure out something.

It is easy to find a gas station in most places today.

Why were there fewer gas stations in 1915 than today?

____

____

____

____

____

____

Riding in a Model T

The Model T was popular for many reasons. One reason was because it did not break down as much as other cars. The Model T did have some problems. It didn't go very fast, and it didn't brake very well.

Tires blew out more often than they do today. This was a bother. It kept people from getting to places. It could also be hard to find help. There were fewer gas stations and mechanics in 1915. People learned how to fix and change their own tires.

mechanics people who fix cars

popular liked by many people

Question
Ask yourself questions about what you do not understand. Reread to find the answers.

I wonder, Why are cars safer today? I read the page again. One reason is because they have seat belts.

Write a question you have about this part of the article.

____

____

____

____

____

Changes in Cars

The Model T was not as safe as today's cars. It had no seat belts to keep people in place. It had no **turn signals** to show when the car was about to turn. Today's cars have both of these things.

The early cars changed in other ways, too. Windows were added to the doors. This didn't let rain and dust from the roads get inside. Over time, cars became less loud and less bumpy during rides.

Cars are still changing. In the future they may look very different than they do today.

turn signals blinking lights on the outside of a car

Cause and Effect

When something happens, it is because something else causes it to happen. What happens is called the **effect**. Why it happens is called the **cause**. Use what you have read about cars to finish the chart.

Effect		Cause
All the Model T cars looked the same	→	because ______________________ ______________________.
People had to fix and change their own tires	→	because ______________________ ______________________.
Cars today are safer	→	because ______________________ ______________________.

Share

Use what you have read to tell a friend how cars have changed.

Make Connections

Think about "Michael's Big News" and "Take a Drive Through Time." Think about how the two selections connect to each other and to you.

1. Write one idea about old cars that you read in both the letter and the article.

___

___

2. "Take a Drive Through Time" tells how today's cars are safer. Name two things that would have made Michael's car trip to the farm safer.

___

___

3. If you could take a ride in a Model T, what would you enjoy about it?

___

___

Write a Letter

Pretend you can send a letter back in time. Write a letter to Michael and tell him about cars today.

Dear ________________,

____

____

____

____

____

____

____

From,

____

When Caterpillars Fly

Why would a caterpillar be called Flutter?

Jo-Jo the rabbit hopped into the garden. Flutter the caterpillar was eating a leaf.

"Hello," said Jo-Jo. "My name is Jo-Jo. You must be new here. What's your name?"

"Hello," said the caterpillar. "I'm Flutter."

"Flutter? Flutter is a funny name for a caterpillar," Jo-Jo said. "Caterpillars don't have wings. They don't flutter."

"Wise Owl says that someday I will fly," Flutter said proudly.

Jo-Jo laughed.

Then Jo-Jo saw Dolly the bird.

"Flutter," said Jo-Jo. "Since you can't fly yet, you should hide," he said. "Here comes Dolly!"

Birds like to eat caterpillars, so Flutter hid behind Jo-Jo.

Jo-Jo sat up. "I love to play hide-and-seek!"

"You like it because no one is looking for you!" said Flutter. They both laughed.

The next day, when Jo-Jo came to the garden, Flutter was not there.

"Flutter is playing hide-and-seek," he said. Jo-Jo looked for days, but he could not find Flutter.

“Look, Jo-Jo,” said Dolly one day. She pointed her wing.

Jo-Jo looked and saw a beautiful butterfly. Its black and orange wings opened and closed slowly.

“Hello, Jo-Jo,” said the butterfly. But it was Flutter’s voice. How could that be?

“I told you I would fly someday,” Flutter said.

“But where have you been?” Jo-Jo asked.

“I have been in my cocoon. Caterpillars turn into butterflies. That’s why I’m called Flutter.”

Jo-Jo hopped up and down. “Can we play now?”

Flutter landed on Jo-Jo’s nose. It tickled, but Jo-Jo didn’t mind.

cocoon a silky covering that caterpillars spin around themselves

Use what you have read to answer the questions. Fill in the circle next to the best answer.

---

1. Why couldn't Jo-Jo find Flutter the caterpillar?
- Ⓐ Flutter turned into a butterfly.
- Ⓑ Flutter moved to a new home.
- Ⓒ Flutter was sad.
- Ⓓ Flutter was at school.

2. Who are the characters?
- Ⓐ Jo-Jo, Wally, Dolly
- Ⓑ Jo-Jo, Flutter, Dolly
- Ⓒ Flutter, Sunny
- Ⓓ Flutter, Harry

3. What tells you the story is **not** real?
- Ⓐ Butterflies cannot fly.
- Ⓑ Rabbits do not hop.
- Ⓒ Animals do not talk.
- Ⓓ Butterflies do not have color.

4. At the end of the story, how does Jo-Jo feel about Flutter coming back?
- Ⓐ unhappy
- Ⓑ worried
- Ⓒ sad
- Ⓓ excited

TESTING YOUR UNDERSTANDING

Butterflies All Around

Butterflies are amazing!
Find out all about them in this article.

There are more than 7,000 different kinds of butterflies in North America. Some are very small. Others are as large as a bird! They come in many different sizes, shapes, and colors.

Travelers

Some butterflies travel many miles. In the fall, monarch butterflies fly from the United States and Canada to Mexico to stay warm during the winter. In the spring, they return. The trip is 2,000 miles each way!

Painted ladies are another kind of butterfly. They have many colors. They live in North Africa and Mexico. In the spring, they travel north. By summer, some can be found in Iceland!

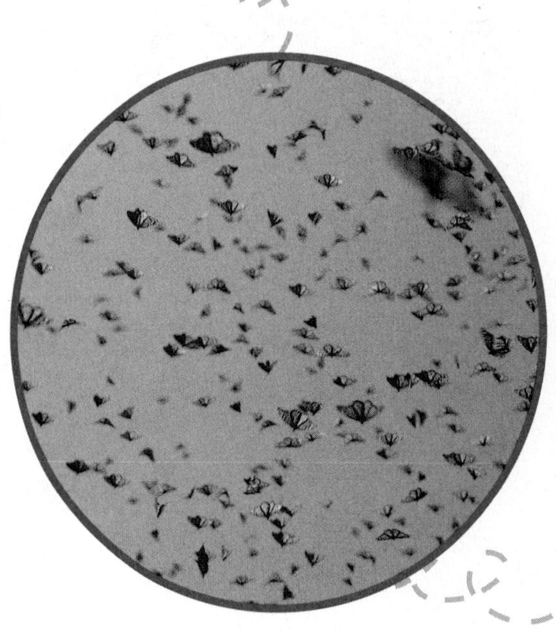

Protecting Themselves

Monarch butterfly

Birds eat butterflies. Some kinds of butterflies can protect themselves. When monarchs are caterpillars, they eat milkweed leaves. Later, when monarchs turn into butterflies, the leaves they ate as caterpillars make them taste bad. Birds know the black and orange butterflies don't taste good, so they don't eat them.

Monarch caterpillar

Painted ladies have a different way to protect themselves. They close their wings. Then their colors are not as bright as when they are open. This makes it hard for enemies to find them.

Painted Lady with wings open

Painted Lady with wings closed

Butterfly Gardens

Looking for butterflies that live near you is fun. It is also a way to learn about nature.

One way to **attract** butterflies is to plant a butterfly garden. In a butterfly garden, there are flowers that butterflies like. Butterflies sit on the flowers and keep warm in the sun. They get food from the flowers. They also lay eggs on the plants. Then there are even more butterflies!

The next time you see a butterfly, take a good look at it. Maybe it came from far away!

attract to make something come closer

Use what you have read to answer the questions. Fill in the circle next to the best answer.

1. Which words help you picture what butterflies look like?

Ⓐ bad taste
Ⓑ bright colors
Ⓒ nice smell
Ⓓ bad smell

2. Why do monarch caterpillars eat milkweed leaves?

Ⓐ because they taste good
Ⓑ to get milk
Ⓒ because the plant has pink flowers
Ⓓ because they can't buy them

3. What is the **best** reason why butterflies are amazing?

Ⓐ They have wings.
Ⓑ They can fly very far.
Ⓒ They eat leaves.
Ⓓ They taste like apples.

4. Which people would make butterfly gardens?

Ⓐ people who scare butterflies
Ⓑ people who eat butterflies
Ⓒ people who have cats
Ⓓ people who like butterflies

Make Connections

Think about what you read in "When Caterpillars Fly" and "Butterflies All Around." Then answer these questions.

1. What do caterpillars eat?

Ⓐ birds
Ⓑ spiders
Ⓒ plants
Ⓓ roots

2. Where do butterflies live?

Ⓐ in gardens
Ⓑ in lakes
Ⓒ in the sand
Ⓓ in the ocean

3. How are caterpillars and butterflies different?

Ⓐ They are the same animal.
Ⓑ They move in different ways.
Ⓒ They like leaves.
Ⓓ They have color.

4. How is Flutter like a real butterfly?

Ⓐ Flutter flies.
Ⓑ Flutter talks.
Ⓒ Flutter's friend is a rabbit.
Ⓓ Flutter plays hide-and-seek.

Write About a Caterpillar

Tell about a caterpillar. What does it look like? How does it move?

Write About a Butterfly

Tell about a butterfly. What does it look like? How does it move?

Best Practices in Reading

Practice Test 1

Student's Name ______________________ Grade ________

School Name ______________________

Teacher's Name ______________________

Test	Items	Possible Score	Student Score
Vocabulary in Context	1–4	4	
Reading Comprehension	5–20	16	
Total	20	20	

I. Vocabulary

Fill in the letter of the word that best fits in the sentence.

1. Lin was very sick. She had to go to the ______.
   - Ⓐ hospital
   - Ⓑ picture
   - Ⓒ student
   - Ⓓ factory

2. Andy watched the bands march in the ______.
   - Ⓐ useful
   - Ⓑ letter
   - Ⓒ parade
   - Ⓓ train

3. The ______ is full of bright flowers.
   - Ⓐ family
   - Ⓑ garden
   - Ⓒ legs
   - Ⓓ blue

4. The workers built a ______ across America.
   - Ⓐ butterfly
   - Ⓑ home
   - Ⓒ money
   - Ⓓ railroad

II. Reading Comprehension

Read each story. Answer the questions that follow.

Fresh Juice

Mike liked to visit his grandma in the summer. She lived in Oregon. It was cool and sunny there.

One day, Mike and his friends were playing baseball. They were all thirsty. They walked back to Grandma's house.

"Grandma, do you have something to drink?" Mike called.

"I have lots of fresh apple juice," Grandma said.

Mike and his friends looked around. They didn't see any juice.

"Where is the juice, Grandma?" Mike asked.

Grandma pointed to the trees in her yard. "It's hanging on the trees!" she said.

GO ON

5. What best describes this story?
   Ⓐ It is about trees.
   Ⓑ It could happen.
   Ⓒ It is about Mike's friends.
   Ⓓ It couldn't really happen.

6. What kind of trees does Grandma have?
   Ⓐ plum
   Ⓑ oak
   Ⓒ orange
   Ⓓ apple

7. What word tells what Grandma is like?
   Ⓐ funny
   Ⓑ tired
   Ⓒ young
   Ⓓ sad

Write your answer on the lines below.

8. Why does Grandma say the juice is hanging on the trees?

____

____

Traveling Apples

Long ago, there were no apple trees in America. Then people from England came to America. They brought apple seeds with them. They began growing the first apple trees in America.

Some people shared the apple seeds with Native Americans. Birds and animals that ate apples also spread the seeds.

A man named John Chapman planted apple seeds wherever he went. He carried a big sack of seeds on his back. People called him Johnny Appleseed.

Today, there are lots of apple trees. Try to eat an apple when you can. They taste good and they are good for you, too!

GO ON

9. What is this article mainly about?
   Ⓐ Apples taste good.
   Ⓑ Animals and birds like apples.
   Ⓒ Only English people planted apple trees.
   Ⓓ Over time, many apple trees grew in America.

10. Who brought the first apple seeds to America?
   Ⓐ Native Americans
   Ⓑ English people
   Ⓒ John Chapman
   Ⓓ Johnny Appleseed

11. How did Johnny Appleseed get his name?
   Ⓐ He ate apple seeds.
   Ⓑ He brought apple seeds to America.
   Ⓒ He planted lots of apple seeds.
   Ⓓ He made apple pies.

Write your answer on the lines below.

12. Why did people from England bring apple seeds with them?

____

____

Rolling Along

Tasha jumped out of the car. She grabbed her mom's hand. "Let's go!" Tasha said.

It was Fun Day at the skate park. Tasha and her mom put on their skates. Then they put on their pads and helmets.

Tasha was a good skater. Mom hadn't skated in a long time. She looked a little scared. Tasha wanted to help her. She skated over to her mom.

"Good job, Mom! You can do it!" Tasha said.

Soon, Mom was skating along with Tasha. Mom had a big smile on her face.

"I used to skate a lot when I was little. This is so much fun!" she said.

Tasha and Mom skated off down the path. Tasha knew they would come back to the skate park soon.

GO ON

13. What does Tasha do on Fun Day?

Ⓐ swim

Ⓑ skate

Ⓒ shop

Ⓓ sleep

14. What does Tasha do to be safe on Fun Day?

Ⓐ She takes skating lessons.

Ⓑ She runs on the sidewalk.

Ⓒ She hangs on to the rail.

Ⓓ She wears a helmet and pads.

15. Why does Tasha help her mom?

Ⓐ She wants her mom to have fun.

Ⓑ She doesn't want to get in trouble.

Ⓒ She has to follow skate park rules.

Ⓓ She wants her mom to go home.

Write your answer on the lines below.

16. Why does Tasha think she and her mom will come back to the skate park soon?

____

____

How Skates Began

Three hundred years ago, a man wanted to go ice skating. It was summer and there wasn't any ice. He nailed wooden wheels to a board. Then he tied the boards to his feet. This was the first pair of roller skates.

Later on, skates had metal wheels. Skates for men had two wheels. Skates for women had four wheels. Ladies wore long skirts when they skated. Men wore shirts and ties!

People liked to skate at places called *rinks.* These rinks had smooth, wooden floors. Skaters could go fast. They could also do tricks on their skates.

Today, people of all ages still like to skate. There are many kinds of skates. Find a pair that fits and go skating!

GO ON

17. When were roller skates invented?

Ⓐ three years ago
Ⓑ thirty years ago
Ⓒ three hundred years ago
Ⓓ three thousand years ago

18. What were the first skate wheels made from?

Ⓐ metal
Ⓑ wood
Ⓒ ice
Ⓓ rocks

19. Why were people able to skate fast at the rinks?

Ⓐ There weren't any speed limits.
Ⓑ People could do tricks.
Ⓒ No one was there.
Ⓓ The floors were smooth.

Write your answer on the lines below.

20. What is one way roller skating has changed?

____

____

Best Practices in Reading

Practice Test 2

Student's Name ______________________________ **Grade** ________

School Name ______________________________

Teacher's Name ______________________________

Test	**Items**	**Possible Score**	**Student Score**
Vocabulary in Context	1–4	4	
Reading Comprehension	5–20	16	
Total	20	20	

I. Vocabulary

Fill in the letter of the word that best fits in the sentence.

1. Lin was very sick. She had to go to the ______.

Ⓐ hospital
Ⓑ picture
Ⓒ student
Ⓓ factory

2. Andy watched the bands march in the ______.

Ⓐ useful
Ⓑ letter
Ⓒ parade
Ⓓ train

3. The ______ is full of bright flowers.

Ⓐ family
Ⓑ garden
Ⓒ legs
Ⓓ blue

4. The workers built a ______ across America.

Ⓐ butterfly
Ⓑ home
Ⓒ money
Ⓓ railroad

II. Reading Comprehension

Read each story. Answer the questions that follow.

Fresh Juice

Mike liked to visit his grandma in the summer. She lived in Oregon. It was cool and sunny there.

One day, Mike and his friends were playing baseball. They were all thirsty. They walked back to Grandma's house.

"Grandma, do you have something to drink?" Mike called.

"I have lots of fresh apple juice," Grandma said.

Mike and his friends looked around. They didn't see any juice.

"Where is the juice, Grandma?" Mike asked.

Grandma pointed to the trees in her yard. "It's hanging on the trees!" she said.

GO ON

5. What best describes this story?
   Ⓐ It is about trees.
   Ⓑ It could happen.
   Ⓒ It is about Mike's friends.
   Ⓓ It couldn't really happen.

6. What kind of trees does Grandma have?
   Ⓐ plum
   Ⓑ oak
   Ⓒ orange
   Ⓓ apple

7. What word tells what Grandma is like?
   Ⓐ funny
   Ⓑ tired
   Ⓒ young
   Ⓓ sad

Write your answer on the lines below.

8. Why does Grandma say the juice is hanging on the trees?

____

____

Traveling Apples

Long ago, there were no apple trees in America. Then people from England came to America. They brought apple seeds with them. They began growing the first apple trees in America.

Some people shared the apple seeds with Native Americans. Birds and animals that ate apples also spread the seeds.

A man named John Chapman planted apple seeds wherever he went. He carried a big sack of seeds on his back. People called him Johnny Appleseed.

Today, there are lots of apple trees. Try to eat an apple when you can. They taste good and they are good for you, too!

GO ON

9. What is this article mainly about?
   - Ⓐ Apples taste good.
   - Ⓑ Animals and birds like apples.
   - Ⓒ Only English people planted apple trees.
   - Ⓓ Over time, many apple trees grew in America.

10. Who brought the first apple seeds to America?
   - Ⓐ Native Americans
   - Ⓑ English people
   - Ⓒ John Chapman
   - Ⓓ Johnny Appleseed

11. How did Johnny Appleseed get his name?
   - Ⓐ He ate apple seeds.
   - Ⓑ He brought apple seeds to America.
   - Ⓒ He planted lots of apple seeds.
   - Ⓓ He made apple pies.

Write your answer on the lines below.

12. Why did people from England bring apple seeds with them?

Rolling Along

Tasha jumped out of the car. She grabbed her mom's hand. "Let's go!" Tasha said.

It was Fun Day at the skate park. Tasha and her mom put on their skates. Then they put on their pads and helmets.

Tasha was a good skater. Mom hadn't skated in a long time. She looked a little scared. Tasha wanted to help her. She skated over to her mom.

"Good job, Mom! You can do it!" Tasha said.

Soon, Mom was skating along with Tasha. Mom had a big smile on her face.

"I used to skate a lot when I was little. This is so much fun!" she said.

Tasha and Mom skated off down the path. Tasha knew they would come back to the skate park soon.

GO ON

13. What does Tasha do on Fun Day?

Ⓐ swim

Ⓑ skate

Ⓒ shop

Ⓓ sleep

14. What does Tasha do to be safe on Fun Day?

Ⓐ She takes skating lessons.

Ⓑ She runs on the sidewalk.

Ⓒ She hangs on to the rail.

Ⓓ She wears a helmet and pads.

15. Why does Tasha help her mom?

Ⓐ She wants her mom to have fun.

Ⓑ She doesn't want to get in trouble.

Ⓒ She has to follow skate park rules.

Ⓓ She wants her mom to go home.

Write your answer on the lines below.

16. Why does Tasha think she and her mom will come back to the skate park soon?

____

____

How Skates Began

Three hundred years ago, a man wanted to go ice skating. It was summer and there wasn't any ice. He nailed wooden wheels to a board. Then he tied the boards to his feet. This was the first pair of roller skates.

Later on, skates had metal wheels. Skates for men had two wheels. Skates for women had four wheels. Ladies wore long skirts when they skated. Men wore shirts and ties!

People liked to skate at places called *rinks.* These rinks had smooth, wooden floors. Skaters could go fast. They could also do tricks on their skates.

Today, people of all ages still like to skate. There are many kinds of skates. Find a pair that fits and go skating!

GO ON

17. When were roller skates invented?

Ⓐ three years ago
Ⓑ thirty years ago
Ⓒ three hundred years ago
Ⓓ three thousand years ago

18. What were the first skate wheels made from?

Ⓐ metal
Ⓑ wood
Ⓒ ice
Ⓓ rocks

19. Why were people able to skate fast at the rinks?

Ⓐ There weren't any speed limits.
Ⓑ People could do tricks.
Ⓒ No one was there.
Ⓓ The floors were smooth.

Write your answer on the lines below.

20. What is one way roller skating has changed?

____

____